the Buenas Song

By David Grover and Aaron Schroeder

Illustrated by Luisa D'Augusta

Macmillan McGraw-Hill

New York   Farmington

Say **buenos días**
When you say good morning.

2

—Good morning.

Buenas tardes
When you say
good afternoon.

Buenas noches is good night

When the day is at an end.

**Buena suerte,
mi amigo**

Means good luck,
my friend.

Buenos días
—Buenos días

Buenas tardes
—Buenas tardes

Buenas noches
—Buenas noches

—Goodbye.